Elrose Hunter and Simor

Daniel
THE LION TAMER

© Elrose Hunter 2008
First published 2008
ISBN 978 1 84427 349 2

Scripture Union
207–209 Queensway, Bletchley, Milton Keynes, MK2 2EB
Email: info@scriptureunion.org.uk
Website: www.scriptureunion.org.uk

Scripture Union Australia
Locked Bag 2, Central Coast Business Centre, NSW 2252
Website: www.scriptureunion.org.au

Scripture Union USA
PO Box 987, Valley Forge, PA 19482
Website: www.scriptureunion.org

Scripture quotations are from the Contemporary English Version published by HarperCollins*Publishers* © 1991, 1992, 1995 American Bible Society.

British Library Cataloguing-in-Publication Data
A catalogue record of this book is available from the British Library.

Printed and bound by Tien Wah Press, Singapore

Cover design: fourninezero design

Scripture Union is an international charity working with churches in more than 130 countries, providing resources to bring the good news of Jesus Christ to children, young people and families and to encourage them to develop spiritually through the Bible and prayer.

As well as our network of volunteers, staff and associates who run holidays, church-based events and school Christian groups, we produce a wide range of publications and support those who use our resources through training programmes.

Daniel lived long ago in the city of Jerusalem. An army attacked the city and Daniel was taken prisoner. The prisoners were taken hundred of miles from their home to Babylon. In Babylon people spoke a different language and worshipped many gods like the sun and moon.

The prisoners entered Babylon through the huge Ishtar Gate. It was blue, decorated with bulls and dragons. Finish the drawing and colour it blue.

The king of Babylon was called Nebuchadnezzar. He ordered his chief official, "Pick out the best of these prisoners and train them to serve at my court. Give them the same food and wine that I have." Daniel and three of his friends were among those who were chosen.

Daniel and his three friends were given new names in Babylon. Follow the lines to their names.

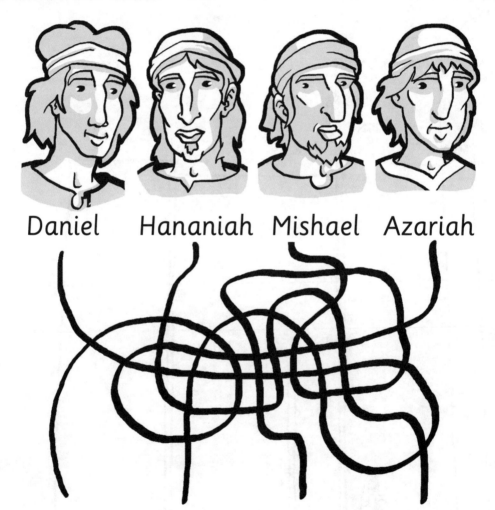

Daniel   Hananiah   Mishael   Azariah

Abednego   Belteshazzar   Meshach   Shadrach

Daniel and his friends asked the official to excuse them from eating the palace food. They believed God wanted them to do this. The official was alarmed. "If you don't look as fit as the others, the king will kill me," he said. "Give us ten days to try it out and see how we look," replied Daniel. After ten days they looked far healthier than the others who had eaten royal food.

Use the code to find out what Daniel and his friends ate and drank.

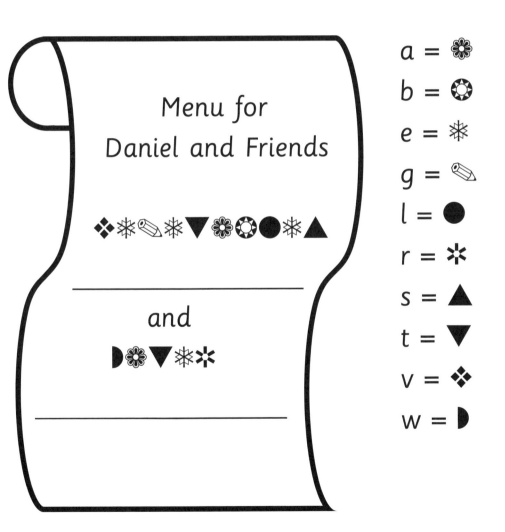

Menu for
Daniel and Friends

❖✳🖉❋▼❀✪●❋▲

_____

and

▶❀▼❋✳

_____

a = ✾
b = ✪
e = ❋
g = 🖉
l = ●
r = ✳
s = ▲
t = ▼
v = ❖
w = ▶

One night, King Nebuchadnezzar had nasty nightmares. He sent for his advisers and wise men. "Tell me what this bad dream means," he demanded. "Tell us the dream, Your Majesty," the wise men answered, "and we will explain it." But the king replied, "No! You must tell me both the dream and its meaning – or I'll have you all killed."

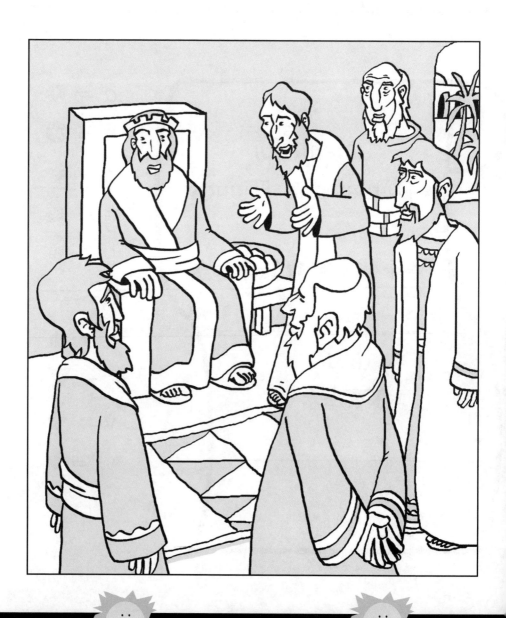

Daniel 2:1–13

The wise men were horrified. "It's impossible, Your Majesty. Only the gods could do this and they don't live on earth," they protested. This made King Nebuchadnezzar furious and he ordered the execution of all his advisers. Daniel and his three friends were not there but they were included.

Look at the two pictures on these pages and find six differences between them.

When Daniel heard about the cruel order, he asked the king for more time. Then he and his three friends prayed to God for his help. God showed Daniel both the dream and its meaning. Daniel was quick to thank God.

Choose the right words from around the page to find some of Daniel's prayer to God.

You give r_____ their p_____ and take it away and you are the s_____ of all w_____.

raiders   powder   rollers   sourc

sauce   windows

winter   spouse

salsa   prayer

power   riders

women   wisdom

rulers   prowler

So Daniel went to the king's official. "Don't kill the wise men but take me to the king," he said. King Nebuchadnezzar looked at Daniel. "Can you really tell me what I dreamt and what it means?" he asked. "God has shown me, Your Majesty," Daniel replied.

Can you match Daniel with the right shadow?

a

b

c

d

e

"In your dream, God showed you the future," Daniel explained. "You saw a huge frightening statue. Its head was made of gold and its chest and arms were silver. The rest of its body was made of bronze, iron and clay. While you looked at it, a great stone came crashing into the statue and it crumbled to pieces. But the stone got bigger and bigger."

Colour the statue using the colours shown in the code.

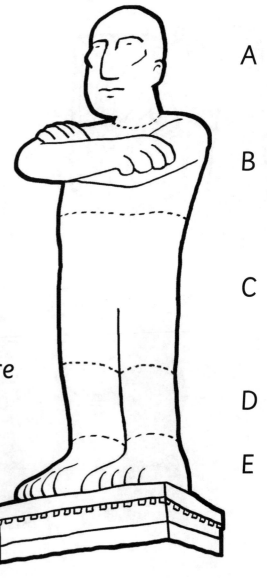

A: yellow (gold)

B: pale grey (silver)

C: brown/yellow
   mixture (bronze)

D: dark grey (iron)

E: grey/brown mixture
   (iron/clay)

A

B

C

D

E

"Your Majesty, you are the head of gold," Daniel continued. "After you there will be other rulers, like the other parts of the statue. These kingdoms will all come to an end. But one day God will set up a kingdom that will last for ever. It will be like the great stone." King Nebuchadnezzar believed Daniel. He even made him his chief adviser!

Complete the ziggurat by adding the bricks in the right order. Then you'll find out what King Nebuchadnezzar said to Daniel.

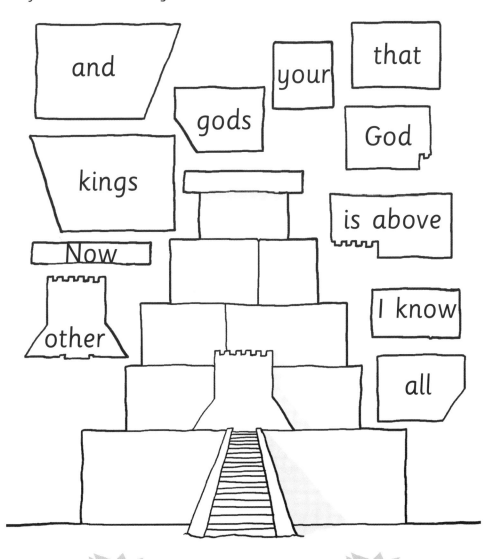

King Nebuchadnezzar was a proud king. He soon forgot that God was greater than he was. The king had a huge gold statue of himself made and ordered all his officials to come and see the statue being set up. A band was ready to play. "When the music starts you are all to bow down and worship the statue," an official announced. "Anyone who doesn't will be thrown into a blazing furnace."

The names of some of the band instruments have got jumbled up. What are they?

TULEF

PETRUMT

_____

PHAR

_____

Daniel 3:1–7

So when the music started, all the people bowed down to the statue – except three men who stood up straight. Shadrach, Meshach and Abednego refused to worship the statue. King Nebuchadnezzar was furious. "I'll give you one more chance," he said. "Worship the statue or be thrown into the fire! No god can save you from me."

Why did the three men refuse to worship the statue? It was because of what God had said in the Ten Commandments. Use the code to complete the sentence.

a = ❀

b = ◉

d = ✓

h = ✂

i = ✳

l = ●

n = ■

o = ✏

p = ▢

r = ✶

s = ▲

w = ◗

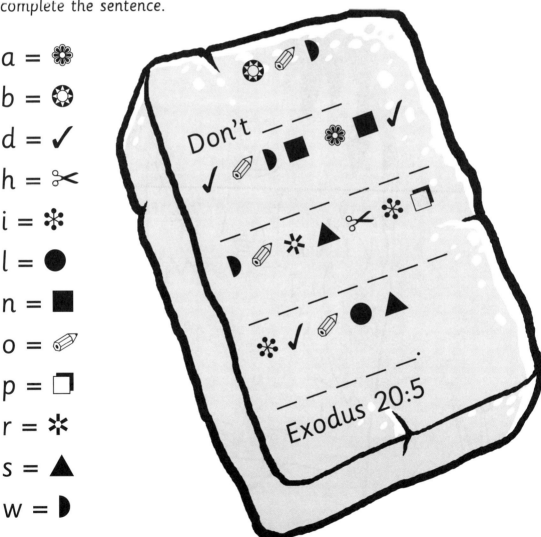

Shadrach, Meshach and Abednego answered the king bravely. "Your Majesty, our God is able to save us from your furnace. But even if he doesn't, we still won't worship your statue." The king lost his temper. "Make the furnace seven times hotter and throw them in!" he roared. His strongest soldiers tied up the men and threw them into the fire with all their clothes on.

Suddenly Nebuchadnezzar jumped to his feet and stared into the furnace. "Didn't we throw three men in there?" he asked. "Why do I see four men walking around in the fire? They aren't being burned and the fourth one looks like a god."

Join the dots and colour in the fire. How many gold rings like the King's can you find in the picture?

Nebuchadnezzar went closer to the furnace and called, "Shadrach, Meshach and Abednego, servants of the Most High God, come out at once!" The three men stepped out of the fire and all the king's men crowded round them. They poked them and sniffed their clothes. Nothing was burnt and they didn't even smell of smoke.

Find these words from the story in the wordsearch. Look across, downwards, upwards and backwards. Put a ring round the words.

FLAMES

STATUE

MUSIC

WORSHIP

SAVE

KING

MEN

ANGRY

V	E	S	J	M	P	O
S	T	A	T	U	E	Q
A	L	U	C	S	B	P
V	I	G	N	I	K	I
E	S	E	M	C	R	H
Y	R	G	N	A	Y	S
L	D	B	E	K	J	R
F	L	A	M	E	S	O
O	H	V	P	F	A	W

Daniel 3:26–27

"Praise the God of Shadrach, Meshach and Abednego!" exclaimed King Nebuchadnezzar. "He sent an angel to rescue these men who trusted him. They risked their lives to obey him rather than me. From now on, anyone who speaks against their God will be killed and their houses pulled down." And the king gave the three men top jobs in his kingdom.

Put the pictures in the right order to tell the story. Put the numbers 1 to 4 in the lion heads.

The next king of Babylon was called Belshazzar. He did not worship God either. One evening he gave a huge party for a thousand people. He even served wine in the gold and silver cups that had been taken from God's temple in Jerusalem. He praised the Babylonian gods. Suddenly a hand appeared and began writing on the palace wall. Belshazzar turned pale and his knees shook with fear. "Fetch my magicians!" he shouted.

How many wine cups, dishes, earrings and pieces of fruit can you see? Put the numbers in the boxes.

Wine cup

☐

Dishes

☐

Earrings

☐

Fruit

☐

When the magicians came in, the king said, "Anyone who can explain this writing will become the third most important man in my kingdom." The men looked at the writing but they were all puzzled. No one could understand it. Then the queen said, "Your Majesty, send for a man called Daniel. He can solve problems and explain mysteries."

What the magicians are saying has got jumbled up. Sort out the words.

When Daniel came in, the king said, "So you are one of the captives from Jerusalem! I have heard that the gods have given you special powers. If you can explain this writing I will make you third in my kingdom."

Cross out every second letter to find out what else the king promised Daniel. Then colour the picture.

Phumrtpflxesrboubnevsm

Grozlidmcvhzapikn

Daniel 5:13–16

Daniel replied, "I will explain the writing but I do not want your gifts. You have refused to honour God who rules from heaven. The writing on the wall is a message from him. It means that your kingdom will end because you have not been a good ruler."

That very night King Belshazzar was killed and a new king took over.

Fill in the missing letters to find out the words written on the wall. Choose from e,i,u.

Hebrew	Words	Meaning
Mene	N_mb_r_d	God has counted your days.
Tekel	W_ _gh_d	You have not ruled as a king should.
Parsin	D_v_d_d	Your kingdom will be split up.

The new king was called Darius. He liked Daniel and put him in charge of part of his kingdom. Daniel did such a good job that Darius decided to let him govern the whole kingdom. This made the other governors jealous and they tried to find something wrong with Daniel's work. But they failed because Daniel was honest and reliable. Then they had an idea.

Use the code to finish the sentence and discover the plotters' idea.

Let's _ _ _ to _ _ _ _ _ Daniel _ _ _ because _ _ his _ _ _ _ _ in _ _ _.

a = ❀   n = ■

c = ✘   o = ✐

d = ✓   r = ✳

f = "   s = ▲

g = ✐   t = ▼

h = ✂   u = ◆

i = ✳   y = ✈

So they plotted a trap for Daniel and went to see King Darius. "Your Majesty, all your officials agree that you should make a law that forbids anyone from praying to any god except you for the next month. And anyone who breaks this law should be thrown into a pit of lions. Have this law written and sign it so it cannot be changed."

Can you find six things that should not be there in this picture of the plotters talking to King Darius?

Darius thought this was a good idea so he made the law. Daniel heard about the new law but he went on praying to God. His enemies saw him kneeling at his open window three times a day as he had always done. They went back to the king. "Didn't you make a law that forbids anyone to pray to anyone except you for 30 days?" they asked. "Yes, that's right," agreed the king.

Find eight changes in the picture of Daniel praying to God after the law

Before

"That man, Daniel, who was brought here as a captive, does not obey your law," the men said. "He still prays every day." King Darius was very upset and did his best to think of how to save Daniel from the pit of lions. "No one can change the law, not even you," the men reminded Darius. So the king sadly gave orders for Daniel to be thrown into a pit of lions and the entrance was secured with the king's seal.

Use the code to find out what King Darius said to Daniel before he was thrown into the pit of lions.

	1	2	3	4	5
A	b	d	y	v	f
B	g	i	t	h	l
C	p	a	o	n	r
D	u	s	c	e	w

A3 C3 D1   B4 C2 A4 D4
"___   ____

A1 D4 D4 C4

____

A5 C2 B2 B3 B4 A5 D1 B5

_____

3 C3   A3 C3 D1 C5   B1 C3 A2   C2 C4 A2   B2

_ __   ____   ___,   ___   __

1 C5 C2 A3   B3 B4 C2 B3   B4 D4   D5 B2 B5 B5

____   ____   __   ____

5 D4 D2 D3 D1 D4   A3 C3 D1

_____   ___.

Daniel 6:13–17

That night the plotters were happy but King Darius was miserable. He couldn't eat or sleep. At dawn he ran to the pit and called out, "Daniel, was your God able to save you from the lions?"

Put the words in the right order to see what Daniel said to Darius.

"___ ___ ___ ___ ___ ___ ___

___ ___ ___ ___ ___."

Daniel 6:18–20

"Your Majesty," answered Daniel, "God sent his angel to shut the mouths of the lions. He knew that I have never done anything to hurt you." King Darius was delighted to hear Daniel and gave orders for him to be pulled up out of the pit.

Draw King Darius' face looking through the hole into the pit.

Daniel's trust in God had kept him from being harmed. The king ordered that the men who had plotted against Daniel should be thrown into the pit of lions. This time there was no angel to save them from the hungry animals.

Join the dots, then finish and decorate the border.

Daniel 6:24

King Darius sent a message to all the people in his empire, commanding them to worship Daniel's God.

"He is the <u>living</u> <u>God</u>,
the one who <u>lives</u> for <u>ever</u>.
His <u>power</u> and his <u>kingdom</u>
will never <u>end</u>.
He <u>rescues</u> people
and sets them <u>free</u>
by working <u>great</u> <u>miracles</u>."

Find the underlined words from the message in the wordsearch. Look across, downwards, upwards and backwards. Put a ring around them.

L	F	R	E	G	K	S	O
I	I	E	P	O	W	E	R
V	S	V	A	D	G	L	E
I	M	E	E	R	F	C	S
N	L	R	W	S	R	A	C
G	R	E	A	T	B	R	U
C	A	K	N	S	M	I	E
K	I	N	G	D	O	M	S

Answers

Page 4: Daniel – Belteshazzar; Hananiah – Shadrach; Mishael – Meshach; Azariah – Abednego

Page 5: vegetables, water

Page 6: angry king, grovelling advisers, border on wall, door outside, pineapple, rug

Page 8: rulers, power, source, wisdom

Page 9: shadow b

Page 11: Now I know that your God is above all other gods and kings

Page 12: flute, harp, trumpet

Page 13: Don't bow down and worship idols

Page 15: Ten rings

Page 16:

V	E	S	J	M	P	O
S	T	A	T	U	E	Q
A	L	U	C	S	B	P
V	I	G	N	I	K	I
E	S	E	M	C	R	H
Y	R	G	N	A	Y	S
L	D	B	E	K	J	R
F	L	A	M	E	S	O
O	H	V	P	F	A	W

Page 17:

Page 18: 8 cups, 4 dishes, 7 earrings, 5 fruit

Page 19: We have no idea what this writing means

Page 20: purple robes and a gold chain

Page 21: numbered, weighed, divided

Page 22: Let's try to catch Daniel out because of his trust in God

Page 23: mp3 player, clock, light switch, book, watch, bottle cork

Page 24: palm branch, pattern in window, pattern on large jar, different small jar, stripe on Daniel's robe, top of Daniel's robe, stripe on rug, four more faces at the window!

Page 25: "You have been faithful to your God, and I pray that he will rescue you."

Page 26: "God knew that I was innocent."

Page 29:

L	F	R	E	G	K	S	O
I	I	E	P	O	W	E	R
V	S	V	A	D	G	L	E
I	M	E	E	R	F	C	S
N	L	R	W	S	R	A	C
G	R	E	A	T	B	R	U
C	A	K	N	S	M	I	E
K	I	N	G	D	O	M	S

Discover more Bible stories with these great puzzle books!

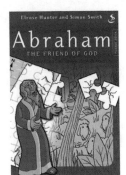

Abraham
The Friend of God

£2.50
978 1 84427 347 8

Joseph
The Incredible
Dreamer

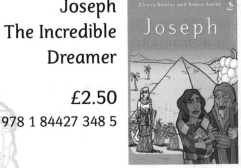

£2.50
978 1 84427 348 5

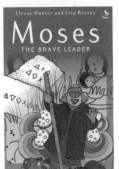

Moses
The Brave Leader

£2.50
978 1 84427 075 0

David
The Giant Killer

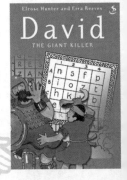

£2.50
978 1 84427 076 7

Jesus
The Amazing
Miracle Maker

£2.50
978 1 84427 077 4

Peter
The Fisher of Men

£2.50
978 1 84427 350 8

Paul
The Fearless
Adventurer

£2.50
978 1 84427 078 1